D0522112

This is a Parragon Book.

© Parragon 1997.

Parragon
13-17 Avonbridge Trading Estate
Atlantic Road, Avonmouth
Bristol BS11 9QD

Produced by The Templar Company plc,
Pippbrook Mill, London Road, Dorking,
Surrey RH4 1JE

Written by Robert Snedden
Illustrated by Peter Bull Art Studio
Series Designer Mark Summersby

Printed and bound in the UK

ISBN 0 7525 1669 8

FRESHWATER
FISH

P

PARRAGON

CONTENTS

INTRODUCTION

Fish are unfamiliar creatures to many people, living as they do in what is, to us, an alien environment. They are usually seen motionless on the fishmonger's slab, struggling for their lives in a net or on the end of a fishing line. The living fish may perhaps be only glimpsed as it rises to the surface of a pond or stream to take an insect on the water, before sliding back silently beneath to its secret existence.

Fish spend their entire lives in water and indeed they can not survive for long outside it. They are as well-adapted to their aquatic existence as we are to our air-breathing one. Whereas we take oxygen from the air through our lungs, fish take the oxygen they need from the water via their gills. Like our lungs, the gills of a fish are richly supplied with blood vessels, which absorb the life-giving oxygen and expel waste gases into the water.

The sleek, streamlined body of a fish is adapted for movement in the water. The fish manoeuvres easily through the water with a flick of the tail to provide propulsion and using its fins to give stability and direction. Within the body of almost all species of fish is an organ called a swim bladder that gives the fish buoyancy and allows it to maintain its position at different depths in the water.

There are perhaps 20,000 species of fish in the world and around a quarter of those are found in freshwater environments. Some fish, such as the salmon and the freshwater eel, move between salt and fresh water at different stages in their life cycles. In this book we look at just 38 of the freshwater fish found in the inland and estuary waters of Britain.

As with all wildlife watching, if you are looking for a particular fish it is as well to familiarise yourself with the type of location it favours. It is not impossible that you might find a fish of fast-moving rivers such as the chub in the still waters of a canal, or an estuary fish such as the shad in the headwaters of a river but the chances are certainly diminished.

Undoubtedly one of the best ways to learn the habits of a fish is to set out to catch it! A successful angler will be thoroughly familiar with the lifestyle of the specimen fish he wishes to catch, choosing his spot on riverbank or lake carefully to maximise his chances and pitting his skills against those of the fish.

It is beyond the scope of this book to teach you how to catch fish. If you wish to learn, it would be a good idea to find out if you have a local anglers' association. There will doubtless be no shortage of people willing to teach you the rudiments of this most popular of outdoor pursuits.

RIVER LAMPREY

Also known as the lampern, the eel-like river lamprey grows to a length of around 50cm. They are found in rivers and streams throughout Britain and Ireland, and for part of their lives they are also found in the sea.

The lamprey is a parasite on other fish. It fastens itself to its prey by rasping a hole in the fish with a row of sharp, horny teeth and attaching itself with its sucker-like mouth. It will feast on blood while the helpless host fish swims on. A substance secreted by the lamprey stops the fish's blood from clotting, ensuring that the flow of food continues. While it is feeding it breathes by taking in water through the seven gill openings behind its head.

The adult river lamprey spends a year or two at sea. It returns to the rivers and streams to spawn, perhaps hitching a ride on a salmon, which also supplies food for the journey. As the lamprey proceeds upriver it stops feeding. Spawning usually takes place between February and June, the male making holes in stony river bottoms for the female to lay her eggs. After spawning the adults die. The blind, toothless larvae become mature after two to five years and swim out to sea to attain their full adult size.

Opinions differ as to the lamprey's suitability as a food fish. King Henry I is said to have died as a result of over indulgence in lampreys!

BROOK LAMPREY

The brook lamprey is very similar in appearance to the river lamprey and has a similar life cycle. The best way to tell the two apart is by looking at the dorsal fin. The brook lamprey has a single continuous dorsal fin, whereas the river lamprey has two distinct fins.

Unlike the river lamprey, the brook lamprey spends its whole life in freshwater. It can be found in the upper waters of brooks and streams throughout the British Isles. It is the smallest British lamprey, growing to a length of about 25cm, and also the most common. It has no scales and is dark brown or grey.

Like the river lamprey, the brook lamprey has a sucker-like mouth but it lacks the rasping teeth for attaching itself to prey fish, having only a few blunt teeth. The mouth, and the seven round gill openings behind its head, also found on the river lamprey, readily distinguish it from the similarly-shaped eel.

Spawning can take place any time between March and June, the exact period being determined by the temperature of the water. During spawning, masses of coiling fish may be seen, the male fish grasping the larger females with their sucker mouths and twining themselves around them. The female lamprey lays around 1200 eggs in a nest prepared by the male.

The larvae that hatch from the eggs about three weeks later are called prides. They take five years to attain mature adulthood, in the meantime living in the silt of the riverbed and feeding by straining tiny particles of food from the water and from the mud. The adult brook lamprey does not feed at all and dies shortly after spawning.

SHAD

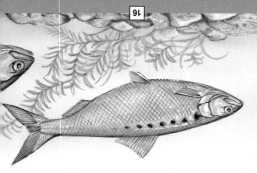

Although shad are primarily sea fish, they spend most of their lives in salt water and are relatives of the herring, a true marine fish, they do have to enter fresh water in order to breed. Some populations of shad are isolated in freshwater and do not enter the sea at all. Shad grow to around 60cm in length and can weigh around 1.4kg.

Every year, the adult shad swim into rivers from the sea to breed and lay their eggs. After spawning the adults return to the sea. The females produce many eggs, which generally hatch within two weeks of spawning.

The juvenile fish that emerge may stay in the river for a year or more, at first feeding on microscopic plankton and later attacking the fry of other fish. They will then follow the current down to the sea to begin the marine part of their existence.

The most common type of shad is the twaite shad, a slender blue and silver fish, shown here on the left. It is found throughout Europe from Norway to Turkey. It can be identified by the row of six to eight blotches along its sides. On the right is the scarcer allis shad, which has a similar colouring to the twaite shad but is distinguished by a single large blotch behind the gills and sometimes a few fainter markings behind that. Both species have a row of toothed scales along the belly.

ATLANTIC SALMON

The magnificent Atlantic salmon spends most of its life in the ocean, but it is born, and usually dies, in freshwater. A fully-grown salmon may be 120cm long and can weigh 27kg or more.

The salmon starts life as an alevin, hatching between 90 and 130 days after spawning. Over the next two to five years it progresses from fry to parr, foraging for microscopic plant life. After about a year, sometimes three, as a parr, the salmon becomes a silvery smolt, about 18cm long, and migrates to the sea. After several years in the North Atlantic, the salmon returns on a journey of thousands of kilometres to the river in which it was born. Salmon do not feed in freshwater and the journey upriver to the spawning grounds can be arduous, perhaps involving 3-metre leaps up waterfalls. When they reach the headwaters the female salmon scrapes a hollow, called a 'redd', in the river bottom in which to spawn. The eggs are fertilised by the male. The female then fans the loose gravel with her tail to cover the eggs. After this most will die, exhausted. Only the very strongest will make it back to the sea.

BROWN TROUT

Trout can be found in a wide range of waters, but prefer water that is clean, cold and well-oxygenated, with a good supply of food. The brown trout grows to a metre in length and shows a wide variety of colourings, although most have a rich green-brown or black and brown back, lighter brown flanks and a yellow belly, with black and red spots on the body.

Male brown trout reach maturity at two years old, the females a year later.

The adults move from the deeper water of rivers and lakes, where they spend most of their time, to shallower streams to spawn, usually in the winter. The female scrapes a hollow in the stream bed for her eggs and, after the male fertilises them, she covers them over. The young trout larvae, or alevins, hatch in around eight weeks. As they grow they feed on insect larvae and other water creatures, including the larvae and fry of other fish. Adult trout will also leap from the water to take winged insects, a habit that has led to many a trout's downfall on the end of the fly fisherman's hook.

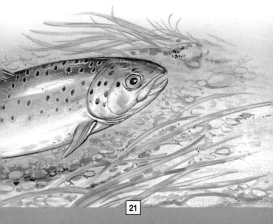

SEA TROUT

After reaching maturity, some trout migrate from the rivers to estuaries and coastal waters to become sea trout. The sea trout is a very close relation of the brown trout, indeed the two are really varieties of the same species rather than completely separate fish, but the sea trout has a different appearance and it behaves somewhat differently as well.

Around Britain, sea trout are found in most of the cold, clean rivers in Scotland and mainly in the western rivers of England and Wales during the spawning season.

The overall appearance of the sea trout is salmon-like, it is a sleek, silvery fish and has small black spots on the upper parts of its body rather than the red and black spots of the brown trout. At spawning time, the sea trout takes on a distinctly darker coloration. The tail is squared off and does not fork.

The sea trout grows to a larger size than does the brown trout, reaching a length of up to 140cm, as it has a richer diet of small fish than does its river-dwelling relative.

The adult sea trout spends most of its life in the sea but will swim up rivers to reach its spawning grounds in the winter. Like the brown trout, the sea trout chooses shallow streams in which to breed and brown and sea trout frequently interbreed successfully.

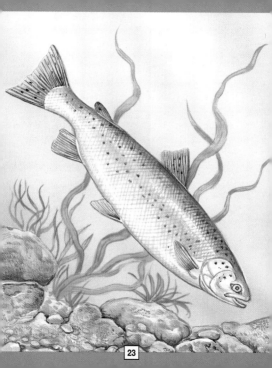

ARCTIC CHAR

Although the char is a sea-going fish throughout much of its range, being found in the waters of the North Atlantic around Iceland and Norway, the British population is land-locked, and is restricted to only a few Scottish lochs, parts of the Lake District, and a couple of locations in Wales.

The char is similar in appearance to its relatives the salmon and trout, but

it is a much smaller fish than either of them, the adult char reaching a length of around 30cm and weighing approximately 0.5kg.

The British char divide into two groups, those fish which spawn in autumn, in shallow water, and those which spawn in late winter in deeper water. The groups are not necessarily divided geographically – both types of char are found in Lake Windermere, for example.

Outside the breeding season the male char is blue-black with a pale yellow belly. The female is generally duller with a smaller head. The back and sides of both males and females are covered in red and white spots. The breeding male is a highly colourful fish, his belly and fins becoming a deep orange-red during the spawning season.

The eggs are laid in a scrape on the gravel bottom of the lake made by the female. Char take four to five years to reach maturity. They live mainly on small freshwater crustaceans.

POWAN

The powan, or common whitefish, is another member of the salmon family, one of the group of fish called the whitefish. It is found in a few scattered places throughout the British Isles. The wide separation of its population has led to it being given different names in different localities – it is called the

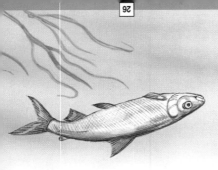

powan in Loch Lomond, where it frequently falls prey to the pike population, while in Wales it is the gwyniad and in the Lake District it is the skelly, but these are all the same species.

The powan is a slim, silvery fish, somewhat resembling the herring. It generally reaches a length of about 20cm, although in places where its plankton food is abundant it may reach twice this length or more. It has a deeply-forked tail and a blue-green back and dark dorsal fin and tail fins. It is distinguished from its close relative the vendace by that fish's upturned lower jaw. In Britain, the vendace is found only in parts of the Lake District, the south of Scotland and Northern Ireland. The powan is found only in deep, clean waters. It is extremely sensitive to pollution and its numbers have fallen off drastically since the Industrial Revolution.

Powan spawn between October and January, the females laying anything from 1000 to 30,000 eggs on the gravel bed of the river. The eggs hatch around 100 days later. The young eat mostly plankton and the adults will also take invertebrates.

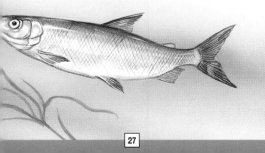

GRAYLING

The grayling is found throughout Northern Europe, but it is only found in a few scattered locations in Britain, from Scotland to the West Country. It favours clean, swift-flowing rivers and lakes. Much of its distribution in Britain is due to its deliberate introduction by people into various lakes and rivers, as it has a reputation as a good sporting fish. It reaches a length of around 55cm and a weight of about 2.3kg in favourable conditions.

The grayling is an unmistakable fish. It has a high dorsal fin with a chequered pattern, used like a sail to maintain its position in fast water, neat rows of silvery scales covering its body and an overall purple sheen.

Grayling spawn in the spring, between March and May. The eggs are laid in shallow water in a scrape prepared by the female. While the female is shedding her eggs the male curls his large dorsal fin around her, keeping the two fish close together and helping to ensure that the eggs will be fertilised. The eggs hatch around three weeks later.

The young grayling grow quickly on a diet of river-bed molluscs and crustaceans and other creatures and sometimes consume the eggs of other

fish. The grayling matures at from three to four years old. Young grayling frequently swim together in tight shoals.

A freshly-caught grayling is said to have a smell similar to that of the garden herb thyme.

SMELT

In Britain, the smelt is a fish of coastal waters and estuaries, entering fresh water only in order to spawn, although there are some inland populations in other parts of Europe. It is a slim-built, silvery fish, with a green tinge to its back, reaching a length of around 45cm. The dorsal fin is set well back towards the tail.

The smelt is a large-mouthed fish, catching crustaceans and the young of other fish with its needle-sharp teeth. In the sea they will eat shrimps and young cod and herring.

Smelt generally reach their spawning sites in spring, around March and April. The small yellow eggs have sticky stalks, by which they are attached to weeds and stones. The young fish spend the summer in fresh water before moving back downriver to the estuaries.

PIKE

The largest of Britain's freshwater fish and the top predator in many lakes and rivers, the pike is a sleek and efficient hunter. An adult female pike can reach over a metre in length and weigh over 20kg; the male fish, however, are much smaller, rarely topping 4.5kg.

The long green-brown body of the pike is marked with bronze shading and spots that provide it with excellent camouflage as it waits motionless among water weeds, ready to make a lightning-fast strike at its prey, whether it be fish, frog, rat or bird, gripping it inescapably with its strong teeth.

Pike usually spawn around February to April in shallow areas with heavy weed cover. A particularly large female may lay close to half a million eggs, but of course only a few of these will actually survive long enough to produce adult pike. The egg clusters are attached to plant stems and stones.

The larvae hatch after 10 to 15 days, but remain attached to the plant stems by their heads for another ten days or so, as they absorb the yolk from their egg sacs, before becoming free-swimming fish. Large numbers of the young fish die in the competition for food and cannibalism among the juvenile pike is common.

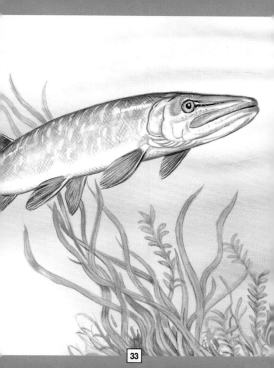

ROACH

The roach is the most widespread of Britain's freshwater fish, being found everywhere from the south of England to the Scottish Highlands, in fast-running rivers as well as still lakes and reservoirs,

although fast-flowing streams suit them best. It is also the fish that is most commonly caught by anglers.

The roach has a purple-black back, large silvery scales on its flanks and orange-red fins. Juvenile fish or fish in poor condition have pinkish fins. The usual length is around 20cm, but some specimens may reach 35cm or more; roach weighing more than 1.4kg are rare.

The roach can be distinguished from the similar rudd by its longer top jaw, and the rudd's longer lower jaw, and from the position of its dorsal fin, which is directly above the pelvic fins. Roach will usually spawn in May, when the water temperature rises above 14°C, but this can vary depending on local weather conditions. At spawning time the males develop small grey-white projections on their heads, called tubercles. These will have disappeared again by July. The eggs are deposited in shallow water, where they stick to water weeds, and hatch about a week later.

The young roach may be seen in dense shoals and many will fall victim to pike and other fish. Roach tend to stay in shoals made up of fish of the same age until the breeding season, at which time they will join mixed shoals made up of other roach as well as fish of other species. They have a varied diet of pondweed, insect larvae, molluscs and crustaceans.

DACE

Also known as the dart or the dare because of its habit of darting through the water of the streams it inhabits, the dace is found throughout most of Europe, but in Britain it is is absent north of the border counties of Scotland and from most of Wales. It is most often found in fast-flowing streams and rivers. Dace are rarely more than 30cm in length.

The dace is similar to the roach but is less colourful and usually smaller. The dace's back is greenish-black, the flanks silvery and the lower paired fins are yellow. The tail and dorsal fins are grey and the anal and dorsal fins have a distinctly concave appearance. The yellow eyes also help to distinguish the dace. Male dace become mature after only a year, females take two years before they are able to breed. The spawning season is from February to May, at which time the male develops small white swellings, called tubercles, on his forehead. Dace spawn at night in shallow, running water, each female laying 25,000 eggs or more in the gravel on the streambed, staying around the same place until they shed all their eggs. At dawn, the exhausted males drift downstream with the current to deeper water to rest. The eggs hatch around three weeks later, depending on the water temperature.

Dace feed together in large shoals, probably to give them some protection from predators, their diet including flying insects and their larvae and crustaceans. The young fish will eat some plant material as well.

CHUB

In Britain, the chub is restricted mainly to England and Wales and it is not found north of the border counties of Scotland. Chub mainly inhabit slow-flowing rivers but they can also be found in fast trout streams and, on occasion, in lakes and gravel pits. In Britain, chub reach a length of 60cm and a weight of up to 4.5kg – although fish that are twice this size have been caught on the Continent. The female chub is generally bigger and more powerful than the male.

The chub has a broader head than the dace and is overall a bigger fish. Its cylindrical body is covered with large, dark-edged silvery scales. The paired pelvic fins and the anal fin have a reddish tinge. It has no teeth in its mouth, but instead has a double row of teeth in its throat, which crush its food, ranging from insects and water plants to small fish and frogs.

The spawning season is normally in May. Like the dace and roach, male chub develop small swellings on the forehead during the breeding season. Chub must have flowing water if they are to breed. The females lay up to 100,000 sticky eggs each, and these adhere to waterweeds and gravel and hatch a few weeks later.

The young chub generally swim together in small shoals. Male chub reach maturity at around three years old, females at four.

GOLDFISH

Commonly found in ponds in parks and gardens, the goldfish was introduced to Europe from China in the 17th century as an ornamental fish. Since then numerous escapes and some deliberate introductions have led to the establishment of a wild population in lakes and slow-moving rivers.

Wild goldfish tend to be olive-green or brown in colour, the familiar red-gold colouring of the domestic fish being seen only rarely. The wild variety of the goldfish is sometimes known as the gibel carp. Goldfish are usually around 20cm in length, though they may grow bigger under favourable conditions. In captivity they may live to around 30 years old but it would be unusual for a wild fish to live so long.

Spawning takes place in June and July, but only when the water temperature rises above 20°C for a few days. The female lays around 250,000 eggs in slow or still water among dense weeds, to which the sticky eggs adhere. The eggs hatch around a week later. The young goldfish might be mistaken for the young of the crucian carp.

MINNOW

The tiny minnow is the smallest member of the carp family found in Britain, related to larger fish such as the chub and barbel. Minnows rarely exceed 10cm in length. They are found in most areas, sometimes in shoals of over a hundred fish, in fast-flowing rivers and streams. Minnows only live in clean, well-oxygenated water, so their presence is a good indication of water quality. In summer, they often swim in mixed shoals with small roach and bleak.

The minnow is a slender, silvery-brown fish with distinctive vertical brown markings on the flanks. The belly is yellow or white – in the breeding season the male's belly and paired fins become flushed with red.

The spawning season begins in late May, at which time the male's head becomes darker and tubercles, small swellings, appear on his forehead, as well as the belly flushing. Large shoals of minnows gather together to spawn. The females lay around a thousand eggs apiece in small clumps among the gravel of the river bed.

The young fry eat tiny plankton and the adults feed on algae and water insects. Because they are so small, minnows frequently fall prey to other fish and to birds, such as kingfishers. Their only protection is speed and their habit of swimming in close shoals.

GUDGEON

The gudgeon is found in slow-flowing rivers and gravel pits throughout most of England and parts of Ireland. It is rare elsewhere in Britain. Gudgeon rarely exceed 20cm in length and 110g in weight.

The gudgeon has a dull green-brown back, marked by characteristic dark spots, fading towards a flattened yellow belly that suits the bottom-feeding nature of the fish. It has two fleshy barbels, which it uses to sense food amongst the mud and gravel on the riverbed, one hanging from each corner of the mouth. The spawning season is concentrated around May, but it can occur for a few weeks before and after this time. The females lay their eggs, some 1000 to 3000 apiece over the course of the season, in running water. The eggs, which are large for a fish of this size, are sticky and adhere to stones and water weeds. They hatch about ten days later and the young gudgeon form shoals that stay in the vicinity of the spawning area. The adult fish also swim together in shoals.

Gudgeon reach maturity in about two or three years. They tend to move to deeper waters in the winter months.

Gudgeon are entirely bottom-feeders and will often lie quietly on the bottom, hidden by the stones. Their diet includes various insect larvae, crustaceans, such as freshwater shrimp, fish eggs and some plant material.

RUDD

In Britain, the rudd is mainly confined to lowland areas of England, and is found only rarely in Wales and the south of Scotland. It is most frequently encountered in gently flowing rivers, lakes and canals with quiet backwaters. Adult rudd grow to around 30cm in length and may exceed 1kg in weight.

The rudd is one of the most handsome of freshwater fish. It has orange-red fins, with those on the underside being the brightest, and large bronze scales. The fins are redder and body greener than those of the roach, with which it may sometimes be confused. The head is rather small and the eye is orange-yellow in colour.

The spawning season usually begins in late May, at which time the males become more brightly coloured. Shoals of rudd may be observed splashing around among the weeds. The females lay thousands of sticky yellow eggs, which adhere to the stems of water weeds.

The eggs hatch around a week later and the fry that emerge feed on a variety of tiny organisms. The adult fish's diet includes plant material, insects and crustaceans and the larger specimens may consume fish of smaller species. Rudd can take up to four years to reach maturity.

TENCH

The tench is found
throughout Britain, south
of the valleys of the Forth
and Clyde rivers in
Scotland, but is most
common in the south-east
of England in open waters
such as the Norfolk
Broads and in slow-

moving rivers. A large tench may reach 70cm in length and exceed 2kg in weight. Fish twice this size have been caught on occasion. The tench is distinguished by its green-bronze colouring, shading to orange-yellow on the belly. The scales are small and deeply embedded in the fish's smooth, slimy skin. The fins are rounded and powerful and the tench is overall a thickset and muscular fish. The pelvic fins of the male have a thickened leading edge. A short barbel, which is used for sensing food, hangs from each corner of the mouth.

The spawning season occurs during July and August, after the water temperature

has risen above 18°C for two weeks. In Britain, the tench will not spawn at all in some years if the conditions are not right for it to do so. A large female may lay close to half a million eggs but obviously not many will survive to reach maturity, as they fall victim to predation from other fish and from birds. When they hatch, the fry feed on microscopic plankton and algae. Adult tench eat freshwater mussels, snails and other invertebrates.

In winter, tench go into a state of semi-hibernation, burying themselves in the mud at the bottom of the river or lake at the first sign of frost. They will reappear from time to time on warm early spring days, but are not really fully active again until May.

BARBEL

Originally restricted to the Thames and Trent river systems in Britain, the barbel is now more widespread through its introduction into other rivers as an excellent sport fish for anglers. It is most at home in clear rivers with stony or sandy beds and a strong water flow. Barbel may grow up to 90cm in length and can exceed 4.5kg in weight.

The barbel is a long-bodied fish, shading from greeny-brown to golden yellow in colour. The paired fins are a reddish-orange colour, the others are a duller grey-brown. The scales are all clearly defined. There is some variation in colour amongst barbel populations, depending on local conditions. There are four fleshy barbels, two on the upper jaw and one in each corner of the mouth. These are used for detecting food.

Barbels spawn in early summer, between May and July, among stones and loose gravel on the river bottom. Before this they will have swum upstream, often in large numbers, to find suitable locations for spawning. Afterwards, the exhausted fish find quiet spots in which to rest. The eggs are sticky and adhere to the stones on the riverbed.

Barbels feed on insect larvae, snails and other molluscs and invertebrates, foraging along the bottom of the river, mostly during the hours of darkness.

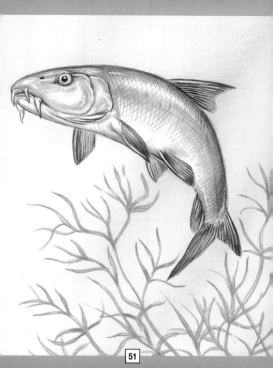

BLEAK

In Britain, the bleak is restricted to England and some parts of Wales, but is more common in other parts of Europe. It is found in lakes and clean, slow-moving lowland rivers and streams. Bleak grow to around 18cm in length.

The bleak is a silvery fish overall, but with a greenish tinge along its back. It has a narrow body, with large eyes and a downward-slanting mouth. Its paper-thin scales, which are shed easily, were once used in the manufacture of artificial pearls.

The spawning season is generally between April and June, depending on the water temperature. In the breeding season, the male develops raised lumps, called tubercles. These usually appear on the forehead but sometimes they are also seen on the rest of the body. The pale yellow eggs are laid either singly or in small groups on gravel beds in shallow water. They hatch around two to three weeks later.

In summer, large shoals of bleak can be seen just under the surface, where they feed on insects and small crustaceans on the surface and leaping above the water to take the occasional flying insect. In winter they retreat to deeper waters.

Because of their small size, bleak are eaten by larger fish and are often used as bait by anglers.

BITTERLING

Although it is fairly common in other parts of Europe, the bitterling is one of the rarer freshwater fish in Britain, being restricted to the north-west of England, where it is found in places such as the Manchester Ship Canal and Wicken Fen. It is thought to be an escape from domestic aquaria. Bitterling are small fish, growing to around 9cm in length.

The bitterling is a colourful fish, generally bronze-green in colour, with a brilliant metallic blue stripe running along its hind flanks to the base of the tail. In the spawning season, the male's colours brighten

even more, taking on a sparkling iridescent sheen.

The bitterling has an unusual lifestyle, being entirely dependent on a living freshwater mussel to complete its life cycle. In spring, the male will select a suitable mussel and guard it. The female develops a long fleshy, egg-laying tube, called an ovipositor, and she uses this to insert her eggs into the valves of the mussel. The male then releases his sperm, and this is sucked into the mussel through its siphon system as it breathes. The pair of fish may repeat the process, implanting between 40 and 100 eggs in a succession of different mussels.

The eggs are protected from predators inside the mussel and hatch two to three weeks later. The bitterling larvae actually live amongst the gills of the mussel for a few days before emerging to take up a more normal free-swimming way of life.

Bitterling feed on vegetation and small water creatures such as insect larvae.

SILVER BREAM

Silver bream are found throughout Europe, although in Britain they are restricted to East Anglia and the Midlands, where they are found mainly in slow-moving rivers and canals and also in some still waters. Silver bream can grow to a length of about 36cm and a weight of around 1.8kg.

The silver bream is a deep-bodied fish. It gets its name from its silver-white colour, which gives it a similar appearance to that of the young common bream. The silver bream can be distinguished by its large eye, set close to the tip of the snout, and by a pinkish tinge to its pectoral and pelvic fins where they join the body. It has a slimy feel and the scales rub off easily.

The spawning season takes place in May and June, during which shoals of silver bream congregate in shallow, weedy waters. The yellow eggs are sticky and they adhere to plant stems when they are laid. The larvae hatch out around five days later.

Silver bream feed on a variety of insect larvae, worms, snails, crustaceans and small plants, either on the bottom or in the middle waters of the river and often form mixed shoals with other fish.

COMMON BREAM

The common or bronze bream is found throughout Europe, although in Britain it is rarely seen north of the Scottish border counties. It is most frequently encountered in the bottom

regions of still or slow-moving rivers and canals, gravel pits and lakes in lowland districts. Bream can grow up to 80cm in length and may exceed 4.5kg in weight.

The young bream is silver in appearance, resembling the adult silver bream, but the adult common bream has a distinctive bronze colouring, with dark fins. The common bream has a deep, flattened body and a relatively small head. The mature fish has a distinct hump, starting behind the head and continuing up to the dorsal fin.

The spawning season takes place in late spring and early summer. Hundreds of fish may be seen forming dense shoals near the surface among the weeds in shallow water during the hours of darkness. The spawning activity can be energetic and noisy, involving a great deal of splashing and rolling. The sticky eggs adhere to the water weed and hatch out within two weeks.

Bream are exclusively bottom feeders, gathering together in large shoals to do so. The fish swims slowly over the bottom, keeping an almost vertical position as it sucks up food from the bed with its tube-like extendible mouth. A feeding shoal of bream will frequently make their presence known by sending up large quantities of bubbling, discoloured water to the surface as they disturb the muddy bottom in their search for food.

CARP

The common carp was originally brought to Europe from Asia by the Romans. It is not known when it was first introduced to Britain, but it was stocked as a food fish in monastery ponds in the 13th century. Today they are found in warm, shallow waters, such as slow-moving lowland rivers and lakes. Carp may reach a length of about 60cm and a weight of up to 9kg in the wild. Domestic specimens can grow to twice this size.

Wild carp are greenish-brown above, shading to yellow below. The mouth has four barbels, one at each corner and two shorter ones on the upper lip. Varieties of common carp include the mirror carp, distinguished by exceptionally large scales along the flank, and the leather carp, which has almost no scales at all!

The spawning season takes place in early summer when the water temperature has stayed at 17°C or more for at least two weeks. The females shed copious quantities of eggs among water weeds in shallow water – a large female may produce a million eggs. The eggs hatch about a week later and the larvae grow rapidly. The adults are bottom feeders, their diet including worms, shellfish and plant material.

The carp reaches maturity at the age of about three to five. They are long-lived fish, often surviving 40 years in captivity.

CRUCIAN CARP

The crucian carp is restricted to southern and eastern areas of Britain, where it is found in small ponds and gravel pits with a rich supply of vegetation and in slow-moving rivers. It has an ability to survive in poor waters, existing under conditions that other fish could not tolerate, but it will only grow to its full size under favourable conditions. Although the crucian carp is really a warm water fish, it shows a great ability to survive cold conditions. It was probably introduced to Britain from Germany. Crucian carp can grow to around 50cm in length.

The crucian carp is a deep-bodied fish with a distinct hump beginning just behind the head and extending up to the dorsal fin. The convex dorsal fin is large and sail-like. Unlike the common carp, the crucian carp has no barbels. It is generally reddish-brown and bronze in colour.

Spawning occurs between May and July when the water temperature has risen above 13°C. The eggs are laid in shallow water, where they stick to the leaves and stems of water plants. Crucian carp and common carp frequently spawn in the same waters and hybrids are not uncommon.

After hatching, the young larvae remain attached to the plants for a day or two while the remainder of the yolk sac is absorbed. The free-swimming young feed on small crustaceans. The adults also feed on plants and insect larvae.

STONE LOACH

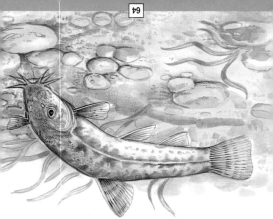

The stone loach is found throughout most of Britain, although it appears to be absent from the far south-western corner of England and from the north of Scotland. It is found in clean, stony-bottomed rivers and streams with a steady flow of water. The stone loach can not tolerate pollution at all and will quickly disappear from waters that are even slightly contaminated, which makes it a good environmental quality indicator. This small fish will rarely exceed 12cm in length.

The stone loach lacks scales and is olive-brown in colour with yellow marbling, which helps to camouflage the fish against the background of the stony riverbed. The male is slimmer than the female and has slightly larger and more pointed pectoral fins. The dorsal and tail fins are patterned by dark spots. The stone loach has a flattened underside, which is an adaptation to its bottom-dwelling lifestyle.

The spawning season takes place between April and June, when the sticky yellow eggs are laid among water weeds and stones, to which they adhere. After about two weeks, depending on the temperature of the water, the eggs hatch out. The young stone loach grows quickly and generally reaches maturity at around two to three years old.

Stone loach feed on a wide variety of bottom-dwelling creatures, such as insect larvae, shrimp and other small crustaceans. The stone loach is a night feeder that lies hidden among the stones on the riverbed during the day. It relies on the six long, fleshy barbels on its mouth, four fringing the upper lip and one at each corner, to find its food on the bottom.

SPINED LOACH

Although the spined loach is a common fish throughout most of Europe, in Britain it is confined to parts of East Anglia and the East Midlands. It is usually found in slow-moving muddy rivers and canals, lakes, reservoirs and stagnant ponds, showing a preference for sites where there is dense vegetation. It is much more tolerant of poor water conditions than is the stone loach and can live in water with a low oxygen content, as it is able to gulp air at the surface of the water and absorb oxygen through its gut. The spined loach reaches a length of around 10cm.

The spined loach has a long, narrow body. It is a light brown colour, paler than that of the stone loach, with rows of darker blotches running from head to tail. The name comes from the retractable two-pointed spines under each eye, which may be a form of defence against larger fish, such as pike. Like the stone loach, the spined loach has six food-sensing barbels hanging from the mouth, but they are much shorter. As in the stone loach, there are four on the upper lip and one at each corner of the mouth.

Little is known of the life cycle of the spined loach, although it is thought to be similar to that of the stone loach with a similar diet. It is active at night, burying itself in the muddy riverbed during the day.

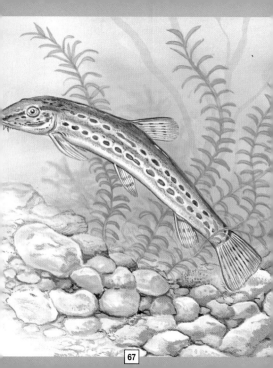

CATFISH

In Britain, the catfish, or wels, is restricted to slow-flowing rivers and lakes, mostly around Bedfordshire and parts of the Midlands in Britain. It is not a native British fish, but was introduced from Eastern Europe. On the Continent, fish of 5 metres in length and weighing over 300kg have been recorded, but in Britain a good specimen will be about a tenth as big as this.

The catfish has a slimy, scaleless body, black or grey-bronze in colour. The

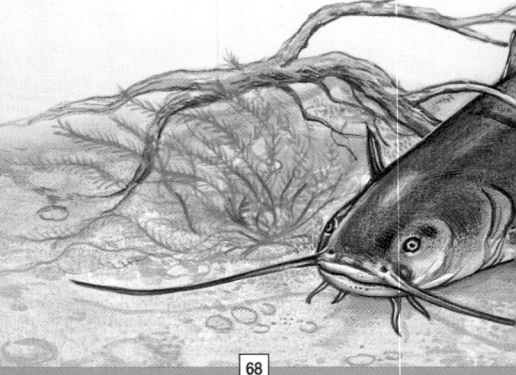

dorsal fin is very small while the anal fin, by contrast, is half the length of the body. The head is broad and flattened, with a large mouth. There are six barbels, the two on the upper jaw reaching back as far as the pectorals.

Spawning usually occurs between May and July, when the female lays up to half a million eggs in a nest hollowed out by the male and sometimes lined with vegetation. The male will guard the eggs until they hatch about three weeks later.

Catfish are predators and hunt in shallow waters at night, taking a variety of other fish, amphibians and small mammals.

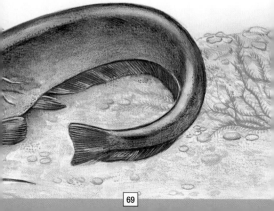

BURBOT

Although it is a common fish on the Continent, the burbot is rarely seen in Britain, and in fact many authorities consider that it may well be extinct or at least close to extinction. The most recent sightings have been confined to eastern England.

The burbot is a freshwater member of the cod family and is generally found in slow-moving rivers and lakes. It grows to a length of around 50cm.

The burbot has a broad head with three barbels, two short ones on the nostrils and one longer one on the chin. It has a long, slender body with a long rear dorsal fin and anal fin. The burbot has a rather drab coloration, being an overall sandy-brown with darker blotches. It is largely a nocturnal fish, hiding during the day and only emerging to feed at night.

The spawning season occurs in winter and early spring, from December to March, at which time the eggs are laid on the sand or gravel bottom of the river or lake, hatching out 40 to 50 days later. Each female can lay anything from 30,000 to 3,000,000 eggs.

The young burbot feed on insect larvae, crustaceans, mussels and snails and reach maturity in around three to four years. The older burbot are primarily predators on other fish and will take gudgeon, perch and roach, as well as other species.

FRESHWATER EEL

The freshwater eel is found in greatest numbers in lowland rivers and fens. Male eels can reach a length of around 50cm and females up to twice this length or more. Eels of over 10kg have been caught in East Anglia. The appearance of the eel changes as its life cycle progresses. The eel's life begins not in fresh water, but in the Atlantic Ocean. Adult eels, grey with silver flanks, with large eyes and small, pointed mouths as shown in the illustration below, swim from the rivers of Europe to the mid-Atlantic to spawn in

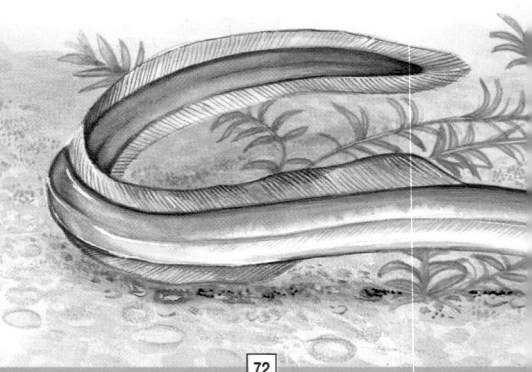

the seaweed-choked Sargasso Sea.

The larvae are flat and leaf-shaped and just 5mm long. They drift north-east on the ocean currents on a journey to Europe that may take four years. On the way the body-shape becomes more eel-like, but stays transparent, with the internal organs clearly visible. The young eels change again on reaching a river mouth, becoming silver-grey elvers, which swim upriver in huge numbers. As they mature the eels take on the dark brown and yellow colouring of the adult. The adult stage may last over ten years before, once again, they change into grey and silver for their journey to the Atlantic spawning grounds.

THREE-SPINED STICKLEBACK

The three-spined stickleback can be found everywhere, from ponds and streams to rivers and estuaries and is a favourite catch of children armed with nets and jamjars. It grows to around 10cm in length.

In the spawning season, the normally brown-green and silver male acquires a bright red throat and belly and blue eyes. He builds a nest on the bottom from plant material and performs a zigzag dance in front of it to attract one or more females. The female wriggles through the nest, depositing her eggs inside, and the male follows to fertilise them.

After the eggs have been laid, the male will stay to guard both the eggs and the territory around them. Later he will also tend the fry, after they hatch one to three weeks later, for the first few weeks of their lives. The three-spined stickleback is the only British freshwater fish to show this kind of behaviour.

Sticklebacks eat a variety of other small water creatures, including insect larvae and molluscs.

TEN-SPINED STICKLEBACK

The ten-spined stickleback is found in estuaries, ponds and streams. It is one of

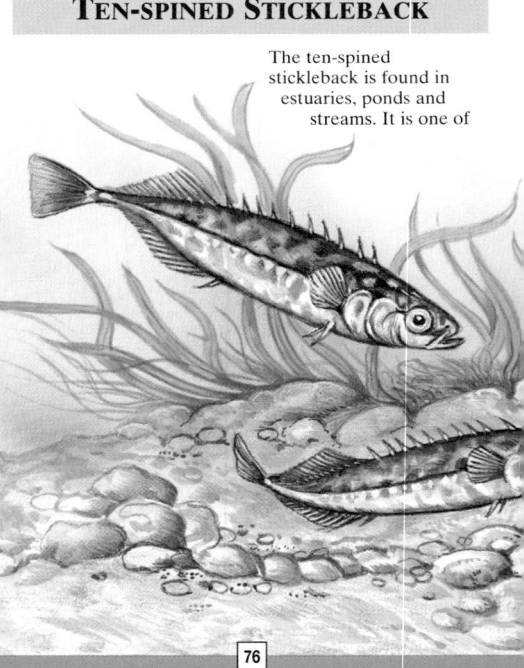

the smallest British freshwater fish, seldom growing longer than about 5cm.

The number of spines on the back of this slender fish can vary from as few as seven to as many as twelve. The back is olive-green in colour and the belly is silvery. The ten-spined is overall a smaller and slimmer fish than the three-spined variety.

During the spawning season in spring, the male fish's throat turns black. He builds a nest from water weed, among the vegetation above the stream bed. The female lays her eggs in the nest and the male fertilises them. He will guard the nest until the young sticklebacks are ready to leave it. When they emerge from the nest, the young fish tend to stay together in shoals, but the adults are solitary fish. A male stickleback will guard his territory aggressively.

Like the three-spined, the ten-spined stickleback feeds on a range of small water animals, such as crustaceans and insect larvae.

PERCH

The perch is found throughout most of Europe, although, in Britain, it is absent from the north of Scotland. It is most often encountered in slow-moving rivers, lakes and ponds in lowland areas. Perch grow to around 50cm in length and weigh about 2kg.

The perch is a colourful fish, purple-black on the back, with dark vertical stripes on the flanks and red-tinged fins on the underside. The first of the two dorsal fins has around 15 spines.

Spawning takes place between April and June, each female laying up to 200,000 eggs in slow-moving shallow, weedy water. The eggs are laid in strands about a metre long, rather than singly, and become entwined in the water weed and the stones on the river or lake bottom.

The eggs hatch 15 to 20 days later. Male perch can reach maturity very quickly, sometimes in just six months. The females begin to spawn at around three years old.

Young perch will eat crustaceans and insect larvae and the adults, particularly the larger specimens, will also take fish of other species, such as roach and rudd.

ZANDER

The zander, or pike-perch, was introduced to Britain from Eastern Europe in the 19th century, since when it has become established in the Fenland region of East Anglia. Its preference is for slow-moving, muddy waters, in rivers and shallow lakes. Zander grow to around 60cm in length on average, but may reach as much as 130cm and a weight of 18kg.

The zander is slim-bodied and silvery-green in colour with a white belly. It has large fins, the first of its two dorsal fins having prominent spines. It has several large teeth at the front of the mouth, as well as many smaller ones.

The spawning season takes place between April and June, once the water temperature has risen above 16°C. A large female can produce upwards of 1.5 million yellow eggs, which are laid in clumps in shallow water among weeds and the gravel on the bottom. Both parents guard the eggs until they hatch out around a week or so later.

Zander reach maturity in around three to five years. They are predatory throughout their lives, the young fry taking crustaceans and invertebrates and the older fish preying almost exclusively on other fish, such as roach, bream and perch. Zander often hunt in packs, harrying shoals of small fish, which they grab by the tail before consuming them.

RUFFE

The ruffe, also known as the pope, is found throughout Europe, but in Britain it is more or less restricted to the east of England and the Midlands. Its favoured habitats are the deeper, more shaded waters of slow-moving rivers, canals, reservoirs and lakes. The ruffe grows to around 18cm in length, reaching a maximum of about 50cm.

The ruffe is narrow-bodied and olive-green in colour, shading to off-white on the belly. It has large fins – the fore part of the dorsal fin has spines. Brown markings on the body, tail and dorsal fins provide the fish with camouflage. It has large purple eyes, which help to distinguish it from the similar-looking young perch, a close relative. It is also duller in colour, over-all. The name is derived from the rough texture of the scales.

Spawning takes place between April and May in shallow water. The females lay strings of sticky eggs that adhere to stones and water weed. In the course of a season, a single female may produce around 200,000 eggs. The eggs hatch 10 to 14 days after they are spawned. The young ruffe grow slowly, taking two years or more to reach maturity.

Ruffe feed on small invertebrates, such as insects and their larvae, and crustaceans. Larger ruffe may also take young amphibians and small fish of other species. They are day-time feeders, finding a safe hiding place among the rocks and stones on the bottom at night.

BULLHEAD

The bullhead is found in the shallow waters at the margins of lakes, in fast-flowing streams and in shallow, stony rivers among the waterweed. It is rarely found in Scotland. Bullheads grow to around 15cm in length.

It has a brown marble appearance. The large fins have spines and there is a spine on top of the gill cases, which make the bullhead difficult to swallow and give some protection from predators. The common name of the bullhead is the miller's thumb. This is derived from the fish's broad, thick-lipped head and flattened body, which is

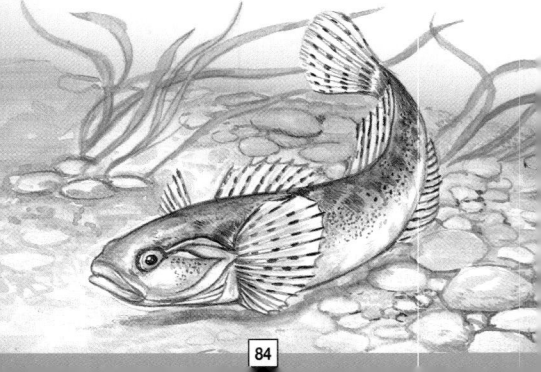

said to resemble the broad thumb of a miller, acquired from rubbing grain between the fingers.

The spawning season takes place between March and April. The female lays between 200 and 300 yellow eggs in a hollow scooped out by the male among stones on the bottom. The male stays with the eggs until they hatch, ensuring a flow of water over them by fanning with his pectoral fins. The eggs hatch around three to four weeks after spawning.

After they hatch, the male bullhead loses interest in the well-being of his offspring to the extent that he may eat them if they stray too close. The bullhead is primarily a nocturnal feeder, emerging from its daytime hiding place among the rocks and stones on the bottom to take water insects and crustaceans. From time to time, small fish and their eggs may also be consumed.

COMMON GOBY

The common goby is the only member of this group of fish that is found in fresh water. It inhabits tidal pools around the coast, but it is also found in estuaries, shallow, salty inshore waters and in slow-moving fresh water channels. Gobies are small fish, growing to around 6cm in length.

The common goby is, overall, light grey to light brown in colour, with a pattern of pale patches and dots on the body that help to camouflage it against the sandy background of its habitat. The pelvic fins are fused together, forming a sucking pad that the goby can use to

cling to stones, preventing it from being swept away by the action of the waves. There are two dorsal fins, the first of which has spines.

The spawning season may be spread over six months, from April to September. The male is highly territorial and conflicts between rivals for a fertile female are common. The victor will guard the female while she lays her eggs and will continue to watch over them until they hatch. During the course of the season several spawnings may take place, with the fish of both sexes mating with different partners. Gobies are short-lived fish, usually only surviving through two spawning seasons. Gobies swim in shoals near the bottom of the waters in which they are found, feeding, in the main, on small crustaceans.

GLOSSARY

alevin: another name for a newly-hatched fish, generally used to refer to young salmon still living on the remains of the yolk sac.

barbels: long feelers around the mouths of some species of fish, such as the catfish and stone loach. Barbels are used to detect chemicals in a similar way to tasting or smelling and are used to sense food on muddy river bottoms and such like places.

bony fish: the name given to the largest and most numerous group of fish, to which most species of fish belong. They are characterised by their bony skeletons and the covering of thin scales on their bodies.

fins: the parts of a fish's body that it uses for moving and manoeuvring in the water.

- the **anal fin** is located on the belly of the fish and is primarily used for balance;
- the **caudal fin** is another term for the tail and is used to provide the propulsion for fast swimming;
- the **dorsal fin** is located on the back of the fish and is also used for balance;
- the **pectoral** and **pelvic** fins are the paired fins on each side of the fish, used for manoeuvring through the water. Jawless fish, such as the lampreys, lack these paired fins.

fry: young, recently-hatched fish no longer living on their yolk sacs.

gills: the part of the fish, located towards the back of the head, that is used to extract oxygen from the water as the fish breathes. The gills have a rich supply of blood vessels into which oxygen is absorbed as the water passes over the gills.

introduction: a fish that has been brought in from outside its normal range and released into the wild.

jawless fish: the name given to the group of fish that includes the lampreys, characterised by their smooth, scaleless skins, lack of pectoral and pelvic fins and absence of jaws.

larva: the earliest stage in the life of many animals, including fish, after hatching from the egg, when it looks different in form and appearance and may have a different lifestyle from the adult it will eventually become.

lateral line: a clearly defined line of scales along the sides of the body of most fish. It marks the position of a system of sensors in pits in the skin that are used to detect movement and vibrations in the water, helping the fish avoid collisions with objects and with other fish when swimming in shoals.

migration: the movement of a population of fish or other animals from one area to another, generally followed by a later return to the original area. Fish, such as salmon and eels migrate, often over long distances, to ensure a regular supply of food and suitable breeding conditions.

parr: the name given to the young salmon during the first two years of its life, when it lives in fresh water. May also be used to describe the young of some other fish.

plankton: microscopically small living organisms, both plants and animals, that float and drift with the current, rather than moving under their own power, in both marine and fresh water environments.

redd: the name given to the hollow scraped in the gravel or sand of a riverbed by fish such as salmon and trout, in which they lay their eggs.

scales: the small plate-like structures that form an outer covering on the skin of most types of fish.

shoal: a large group of fish swimming together, possibly to give a degree of protection from predators. Such a group may also be called a school.

smolt: the young salmon at the stage in its life when it develops silvery scales and begins its migration from fresh water to the sea.

spawn: the eggs of animals that spend all or part of their lives in water, such as fish, amphibians and molluscs.

spawning: to produce spawn.

species: an animal or plant of a particular kind that can be distinguished from all other living things. Opposite sex members of a species can breed together to produce a new generation that will be similar in appearance to their parents.

tubercle: a wart-like swelling or nodule that appears on the head or other parts of the body of some male fish during the spawning season.